Up Bow, Down Bow

FOR VIOLIN   Richard Rodney Bennett

First-position pieces for violin and piano
GRADES I AND II

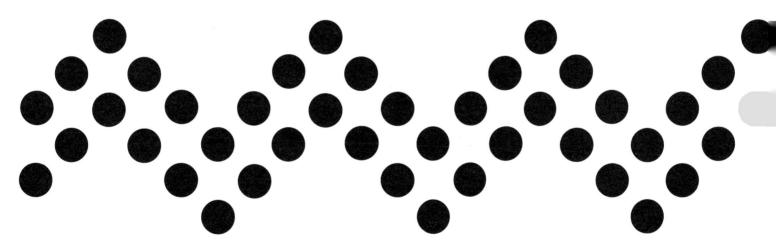

NOVELLO

Order No. NOV 120512

for Michael Easton

These pieces can be played entirely in the first position,
although the third position could be used occasionally.

CONTENTS

Total duration approximately 7 minutes

The composer is grateful to Sally Groves for technical assistance.

Introduction

The gap between starting to learn an instrument and playing 'real' music is a very great deterrent to many players. Consequently, I, and some other composers got together to tackle this problem.

We are producing a series of pieces for many different instruments, playable by musicians with limited technical ability. As a guide, each has a grading similar to those of the Associated Board of the Royal Schools of Music, but I hope people of all grades will enjoy playing them.

Richard Rodney Bennett

Richard Rodney Bennett
Series Editor

UP BOW, DOWN BOW

RICHARD RODNEY BENNETT

1 SERENADE

5820/79

Ped. each bar

senza Ped.

4

2 AIR

3 GHOST STORY

6

45"

Up Bow, Down Bow

FOR VIOLIN   Richard Rodney Bennett

violin

CONTENTS

NOVELLO

Order No. NOV 120512

UP BOW, DOWN BOW

VIOLIN

RICHARD RODNEY BENNETT

1 SERENADE

2 AIR

3 GHOST STORY

4 A QUIET CONVERSATION

5 HIDE AND SEEK

6 A LITTLE ELEGY

7 MERRY-GO-ROUND

Published by Novello Publishing Limited
Printed in Great Britain by Headway Press Ltd   5820/79a   9/93(16268)

NOVELLO
PUBLISHING LIMITED
8/9 Frith Street, London W1V 5TZ
Exclusive distributors:
Music Sales Limited
Newmarket Road, Bury St Edmunds, Suffolk IP33 3YB

4 A QUIET CONVERSATION

8

una corda

1' 20"

5 HIDE AND SEEK

10

6 A LITTLE ELEGY

12

5820/79

1' 25"

7 MERRY-GO-ROUND

14

con Ped.

Published by Novello Publishing Limited
Printed in Great Britain by Headway Press Ltd

5820/79

9/93(16268)

1' 10"